Puppy Intensive Care

A Breeder's Guide to Care of Newborn Puppies

Myra Savant-Harris, R.N.

Dogwise™
Publishing

Wenatchee, Washington U.S.A.

Puppy Intensive Care. A Breeder's Guide to Care of Newborn Puppies
Myra Savant-Harris, R.N.

Dogwise Publishing
A Division of Direct Book Service, Inc.
PO Box 2778
701B Poplar
Wenatchee, Washington 98807
1-509-663-9115, 1-800-776-2665
website: www.dogwisepublishing.com
email: info@dogwisepublshing.com

Graphic Design: Shane Beers Champaign, IL

Library of Congress Cataloging-in-Publication Data

Harris, Myra Savant, 1944-
  Puppy intensive care : a breeder's guide to care of newborn puppies / Myra Savant Harris.
    p. cm.
  Includes bibliographical references and index.
  ISBN-13: 978-1-929242-24-5 (alk. paper)
  1. Puppies--Breeding. 2. Puppies--Parturition. 3. Veterinary obstetrics I. Title.
  SF427.2.H38 2006
  636.7'08--dc22

2005022380
ISBN: 1-929242-24-7

Printed in the U.S.A.

CONTENTS

DEDICATION

This book is dedicated to Dr. Cindy Smith, DVM. The much-loved "Dr. Cindy" has been tireless in her efforts to teach me, share her knowledge and support me when I've had problem puppies. She has taken phone calls in the middle of the night and at the crack of dawn and has met me at the clinic before it opened for emergencies. Her dedication and caring are appreciated more than she can ever know.

My wish for you all is the find a vet like my much-treasured Dr. Cindy.

ACKNOWLEDGMENTS

I would like to thank **L. Calyn Miller** for editing, photography and DVD production. I greatly appreciate his work and encouragement.

HOW THIS BOOK WAS CONCEIVED

Conceived…get it?

My first Cavalier litter consisted of a single little dog puppy, slightly under 3 ounces, who was dumped without warning on the foot of my bed. Once dumped there by his mom she went back to the head of the bed to resume watching her favorite show on Animal Planet. Because she had delivered so prematurely, she didn't have the usual "hormone storm" that would have prompted her to remove him from his sac, chew his cord or tend to him.

Because he was so premature, he lacked a suck reflex so nursing was out of the question. He wasn't due for nine more days so I wasn't set up. Luckily, I had already ordered tube feeding supplies and Esbilac® canned puppy milk substitute, but I didn't have oxygen on hand, no way to keep the puppy warm, no warmed receiving blankets, nothing for cord care — absolutely nothing but the tube feeding supplies. I placed a phone call late in the evening to Dr. Cindy who instructed me on how to care for the puppy. He was much too small and fragile to spend the nights with his mom. She simply seemed unaware that she even had a baby and wasn't showing anything but a vague sort of interest in what was making that squeaking noise. I put a small heating pad between my husband and me at the head of the bed and kept him near us all night. We took turns getting up every two hours to tube feed him.

In no time, I became fairly competent in the art of caring for a newborn puppy in need of intensive care. My experience as a labor and delivery nurse and years spent caring for newborns in neonatal care units helped a great deal. However, when I started looking for resources to give me additional information, I couldn't find a simple, illustrated book that would teach me what to do, show me how to do it, and give me places where I could obtain the things I needed. I longed for a book about all of the things that a breeder needs to know in order to care for premature pups, sick pups and pups that, for whatever reason, no longer have a mom.

I knew how to administer sub-cutaneous fluids, but I didn't know where to find the equipment. I knew how to administer oxygen, but hadn't a clue about where I could obtain an oxygen tank and regulator without a prescription from the vet. I knew that the puppy needed to be kept warm, but I had sort of been counting on the mom (busy watching television at this point) to help me out there. I had been told that Cavaliers were wonderful mothers, but no one prepared me for how they behave if their babies are very, very premature. No one told me that the big white standard poodle on Animal Planet would be way more fascinating than the little wiggly furless baby she dumped on the foot of the bed.

Finally, after spending over 20 years as a registered nurse and 7 years as a breeder of Cavalier King Charles Spaniels, I decided to create the book with a DVD to go along with it that I wished I had with that first Cavalier puppy. I hope together they will give the breeder, or anyone caring for newborn pups, instruction, guidance and, most important of all, encouragement and moral support as you open up your own little "puppy intensive care unit" and begin caring for your sick puppies. With the good assessment tools, equipment and resources described here, I believe that you will be better able to keep your puppies alive until you can reach your vet and get help.

HOW TO USE THIS BOOK

Read the book and view the DVD that accompanies it completely through well before your litter is due. Throughout the book I give you detailed information on the selection and use of the equipment, tools and supplies you'll need to set up your own "warming box" — my term for the box in which you will keep your pups for care.* Give yourself some time to gather the equipment that you will need. Some of which you may already have on hand and most of these will last forever and be worth the investment by saving puppy lives. In the Resource section at the back of the book, I've listed sources for the hard to find items as well as information how to order my own Puppy Intensive Care Warming Box™. After I began teaching others how to use the tools and techniques discussed in this book and DVD, I realized that not everyone wanted to scout out the individual components and assemble their own warming box set up and so, for your convenience, I put together the Puppy Intensive Care Warming Box™ to save you time and effort in getting ready for your next litter.

One more thing: use this book as your workbook. Take notes in the space provided as you learn new things and it will become a valuable reference tool and as well as a source of memories and inspiration for future litters.

*You'll find some differences between the terms used in the DVD and the book, most notably what is called the "hot box" on the DVD (produced prior to the book) is called the "warming box" in the book.

1

WHY NOT BE
AGGRESSIVE??

PULL OUT ALL THE STOPS AND SAVE THE BABY

Statistics tell us that around 30 percent of all puppies born will die in infancy. This shouldn't be all that surprising considering what we know about multiple births in general. The more fertilized eggs there are, the higher your chances are that one of them will have a significant birth defect that will cause their demise. In any litter you run the risk that one or two of your pups may have some sort of a health issue that will require your care.

Many of these pups are going to die in spite of your best efforts. Warming, tube feeding, sub-cutaneous hydration, oxygen administration, even frequent trips to the vet will not save every single puppy. But, for the few that you can save, why not learn how to pull out all the stops, assess all the systems, and "fix" what you are able to fix? Why should you be stuck in the middle of the night, on a holiday weekend, with a raging snowstorm outside holding a sick puppy and no real means of helping him? My goal is to give you information that will enable you to set yourself up with a kind of "puppy intensive care unit." With good emergency care, some specific equipment and these assessment tools at your fingertips, you should be able to keep your loss rate down to around 10 percent.

WORKING WITH A VETERINARIAN

Some of us are lucky and live close to good vets, with emergency vet services available to us 24 hours a day. Great numbers of us, however, live hours away from our vets and do not have access to good emergency services. This book isn't intended to prevent you from seeking the advice of your vet. It is intended to teach you how to help the sick puppy that is born in the middle of the night, on a weekend, on a holiday or during weather that prevents you from reaching a vet's office.

The supplies that I am going to discuss throughout the book are readily available, most without any assistance from your veterinarian. Some may require a prescription and hopefully your vet will cooperate with you in your efforts to save each and every puppy that you have. If not, search for another vet; one who will appreciate that you, as a breeder, have a vast knowledge base about your breed, your dogs, your litter and your puppies. Find a vet who will support you in your efforts to save your puppies, without repeated and costly trips to their office. If possible, work with a "breeder vet" — one who also breeds dogs. They have an in-depth understanding of how much actual work we breeders need to do on our own in order to raise our litters successfully and still be somewhat economical. If you do not have a breeder vet, make every effort to find a vet who is used to working with other breeders in your area. In my area, we are blessed to have both: a wonderful breeder vet, as well as an excellent vet who has a large breeder clientele. Both of these veterinarians have been tireless in their endeavors to teach, assist and support us in our efforts to succeed with our puppies. I can't emphasize strongly enough the need for you to find someone who will work with you to help you learn the skills you need to save your puppies.

WHY NOT LET NATURE TAKE ITS COURSE?

There are breeders who feel, after many years of breeding, that when a puppy is sick, you are better off letting nature take its course and allow the puppy to die. The thought process is that the sicker puppies may be genetically inferior and not appropriate for use in a breeding program. I respect that thought process and don't necessarily disagree with it. However, my experience in health care, particularly with high-risk moms and babies, has given me a different perspective. Many times, a newborn is disadvantaged because of his placement within the womb. If his placenta didn't have the most advantageous location, he may be smaller than the other puppies. If his placenta tore away from his body a couple of minutes prior to birth, he may have been de-oxygenated for too long and may require more vigorous resuscitation than the other puppies. Neither of these things have anything to do with genetics. If his lungs were filled with excessive fluid, you may have to work extra hard on him to save him. Again, this isn't genetic in nature. Environmental factors like these will affect the puppy.

We know that if the puppy becomes chilled, he will not behave normally and the mom may reject him until he "feels" and "acts" like a normal newborn. This is also not genetic in nature, only environmental. My feeling is that as breeders you should have the necessary tools to save a puppy if that is your desire. You should have puppy care equipment and supplies for vigorous resuscitation BEFORE your litter arrives. If you are well supplied, equipped and educated you can make choices as to how you wish to proceed with each puppy. This is what this book is all about: making sure that the choices are yours, and that you are able to proceed in the direction you wish. By the time you have completed the book, you'll know exactly what you need and where to get it all.

My job is to prepare you to recognize when your pup has a problem, be able to assess the puppy in an attempt to identify the problem, and have the materials on hand that you will need to get aggressive in your treatment and care of your puppy. My purpose isn't to try to convince you to function as a vet. It is to convince you to act as a breeder: well educated in all things to do with your puppies.

YOU CAN'T SAVE THEM ALL

You aren't going to be able to save most of the really sick puppies. They are going to die in spite of everything you do for them. Some puppies are born with defects that are simply not compatible with life. We can't see the interior defects, so we make the choice to work hard to give every puppy we produce a chance at life, and we do this knowing that we are going to lose some of our puppies, no matter what we do. With good skills and tools, you can keep your losses down to about 10 percent. Some breeds may be hardier and some more difficult to rear to adulthood, but we can all aim for that 10 percent figure. We don't have to settle for losing a puppy due to dehydration, cold stress, or lack of colostrum. When all is said and done, you will know that you did everything you could to save each and every pup you produce.

2

You Need A
Work Surface

THE WARMING BOX AND ITS MANY USES

You will need to have a warmed work surface on hand a few days prior to the whelping and after that point until the puppies are three weeks old. It is helpful to have your work surface about counter high with a nearby light source. I keep ours on a part of the kitchen counter that has a fluorescent light installed on the bottom of the cupboard. You will need an electrical outlet nearby.

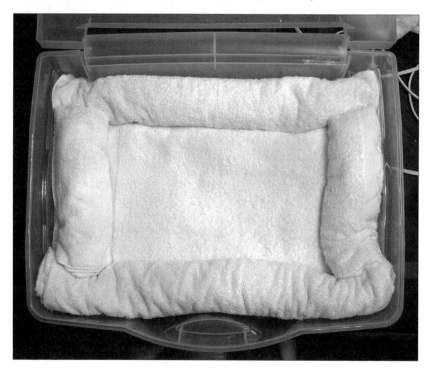

You will use the warming box many, many times during the first three weeks that you have your pups — possibly longer. If the mom requires a caesarian section, take the warming box with you to the veterinary hospital and it will provide a wonderful surface for working on the newborn pups. Surprisingly enough, many animal hospitals are not equipped to handle newborns very well. The staff will be happy to see you come in with your own warmed work surface. Pack an extension cord to keep in the warming box between litters in case you need it at the vet's. There are never enough electrical outlets handy when you need them! If you deliver the pups at home, you will have plenty of uses for the warming box. After each pup is born, you will want to do some cord care, examine the pup and have a safe, clean, warm place to keep the puppies while mom is delivering the siblings.

Anytime that you need to observe the pups or isolate a puppy you will be grateful to have the warming box, plugged in, warmed and set for your usage. You can use it to transport pups to the vet and keep it heated in the car if you buy a power inverter adapter for the cigarette lighter. This device allows you to keep your warming box heated while traveling (see Resources). The warming box will provide a clean, safe surface while your vet examines the puppies. Because veterinary clinics are places where people bring both healthy and sick animals, your vet will be delighted that you have brought the puppies and a warm, clean, safe work surface with you. Neither you nor your vet should remove your puppies from the warming box unless it is absolutely necessary. While the veterinary staff makes every effort to clean the area after every client, puppies left in the warming box will not be as apt to come into contact with unfriendly microorganisms. The warming box will come in handy throughout your puppies' early lives, even when you do a quick clean up on a puppy, because it will keep him nice and warm while he dries.

ASSEMBLING THE WARMING BOX AND SUPPLIES
Here is a list of the things that you will need to assemble for your own puppy intensive care unit. I've put an * next to the items that are included in my Puppy Intensive Care Warming Box™ (see Resources):

Warming box:
- plastic storage box/container* with lid with a hole cut in one of the sides to fit your location. 40 quart/38 liter size is perfect for almost all breeds. Dimensions are roughly 25"x18"x7"
- heating pad*. An inexpensive one without an automatic shut-off feature, approximately 12"x15" size. IMPORTANT SAFETY REMINDER: Always have at least half of the warming box unheated. The pad should only cover about half of the bottom of the box. Always use only the LOWEST setting on the heating pad, and check the temperature of the

box constantly. Overheating the puppies is as dangerous as allowing them to become chilled. Covering only half of the warming box with the heating pad gives them a place to escape from the heat. Remember 95-degrees and you should be fine.

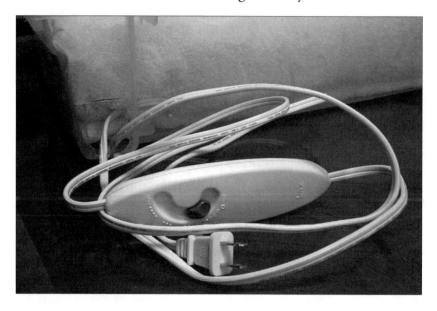

- bumpered crate pad* approximately 24"x18"

Supplies and equipment:
- feeding tubes size 8 French* is a good general size, 10 French for larger puppies
- syringes* for use with feeding tubes
- IV fluid*; my PIC Warming Box comes with 1L Lactated Ringers but your vet may have another preference
- syringes and needles* for sub-cutaneous hydration with ¾ inch or 1 inch needle, 20–22 gauge
- oxygen regulator* (Deluxe PIC Warming Box only)
- oxygen tank full and ready for use
- oral glass thermometer to check the temperature of warming box
- two inexpensive white bath towels to fold and place over the bumpered crate pad
- bulb syringe: 1 oz for toy breeds, 2 oz for medium sized pups, 3 oz for larger puppies
- black felt tipped marking pen to mark the feeding tubes
- prepared milk substitute such as Esbilac®
- pediatric (human) electrolyte replacement fluid such as Pedia-lyte® (unflavored)

- cord care supplies: Betadine, dental floss, cotton balls and surgical scissors
- white washcloths (hand towels for larger breeds), two per expected puppy and several extra
- puppy pads (incontinence pads) 36"x36"
- extension cord

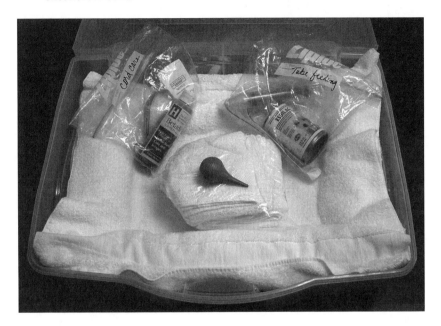

- cotton-tipped swabs
- cotton balls

Optional supplies:
- power inverter (cigarette lighter adapter)
- stethoscope
- Colace® for constipation
- Kaeopectate® for emergency
- Dopram® (prescription required)
- DiaScreen® urine test strips
- rectal thermometer for rectal temp on pups
- petroleum jelly to lubricate thermometer
- disposable latex gloves — use to handle the sick puppy, dispose and wash hands before handling other puppies
- Keflex® antibiotic
- Nutra Stat® nutritional substitute
- Playtex® baby bottle
- Karo® syrup

3

THE RECEIVING BLANKET

OR THE NEXT BEST THING

Now that you have the warming box put together, your next step is to prepare what will function as receiving blankets for your pups. Depending on the size of your whelps, you will need a good supply of either washcloths or hand towels. You will use them for warming, drying and stimulating the newborns.

WHY WHITE CLOTHS?

I suggest buying a new supply of white washcloths or hand towels. You will need to have two cloths per puppy. Many of you are good at estimating the number of pups expected and can be prepared based on your estimations. If your vet has x-rayed the bitch, you will know exactly how many puppies you are expecting. Against a white cloth you will be able to see clearly the blood from the cord stump. The first one will get wet and have blood on it quickly and then you will have a second one to stimulate the puppy further and wrap him as he dries. This will help you to assess blood loss, if any, and assess the color of any fluids that you are able to remove with the bulb syringe. Empty the syringe on to the white cloth for assessment purposes. Have a few extra cloths in the warming box for emergency use. I keep them under the heating pad just in case I need them

Wash the new cloths in a regular washing machine with soap and a cup of bleach. Rinse them twice and dry. Store them in a zipper-close plastic bag in the warming box. Once you have plugged in the warming box in preparation for the delivery (at the very first sign of labor), the cloths will warm while you're awaiting delivery. After the whelping is completed, wash the cloths and store them in the warming box until time for the next whelping.

MY FAVORITE: PUPPY PADS

Once the pups are whelped and cleaned up, I use a product available from medical supply companies and from some pet product suppliers. I call it a "puppy pad" and have found it to be one of the most useful products I've ever found. They are actually reusable incontinence pads such as the type used in hospitals and nursing homes, but they have many, many uses for the dog breeder. Many breeders buy them by the case for use in whelping and puppy pens. I use a stack of them in the whelping box and remove the top one after each puppy is born. That way mom will have a clean surface for the next delivery. Use them in your puppy pens as the surface for the pups and moms. They measure about 36"x36", are washable and last through literally hundreds of washings (see Resources). I housetrain my puppies to the pad and send each pup to his new home with two or three of them. The new owners report nothing but good things about this practice. It's easy to then complete the housetraining process by using the pad as a "moveable" potty area; moving it to the door you wish to use to take him outside to potty then gradually moving the pad outside to the desired location. If you use a puppy pad as the flooring for the puppy pen, they will automatically seek it out when they start to walk around on the floor. Once you start using them you will wonder how you ever got along without them!

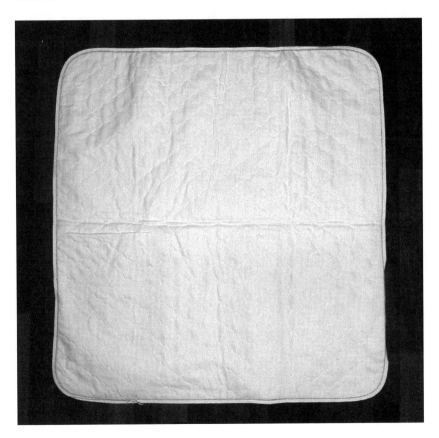

4

START WITH A BULB SYRINGE

MOVE ON TO EVEN MORE AGGRESSIVE TECHNIQUES

While the puppy is in the uterus, the contractions are exerting a "squeezing" effect on him, preparing him to take his first breaths of air. The puppy isn't breathing while he is inside the mom. As long as the delivery goes along normally, the puppy will be born still enclosed within the amniotic sack. Once that is torn open, the puppy should be prepared to take his first breaths on his own without assistance. If the puppy appears to be slow to breathe, or appears to be gasping, you can help him tremendously with the use of the bulb syringe. For puppies, the best thing to buy is the soft rubber ear syringe available in the baby sections of drug stores, grocery stores and big department stores. Toy dogs will need the smallest size, which is usually sold for infants, but larger breeds will do fine with the larger sizes that are sold for older children.

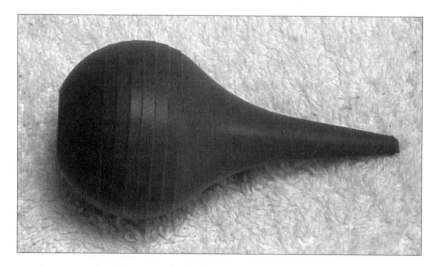

HOW TO USE THE BULB SYRINGE

Remember that the goal of using a bulb syringe is to remove fluids from the throat and nostrils, not to push them further back into the lungs. Press the air out of the syringe to flatten it BEFORE placing it into the pup's throat, THEN insert the tip into the throat and release it to create a suction effect. Practice this several times before the delivery date to get the feel for the correct use of the bulb syringe.

If there has been more than an hour between deliveries, it is a good idea to be prepared to open the pup's mouth immediately upon delivery and syringe the back of the throat. As the puppy is awaiting delivery, his lungs are deflated and filled with body fluids. The squeezing effect of the contractions of the uterus helps to remove part of that fluid. If the puppy sat too long in the birth canal, he might not have gotten the benefits of the squeezing effects of the contractions.

Watching the birth of a human baby, it is often quite surprising to see the amount of fluid that will pour from the nose and mouth as his body is being delivered. If your puppy isn't breathing well, assume that he too has large amounts of body fluids in his lungs, throat and nasal passages. Your primary job at this point is to remove those fluids by every means available.

FIRST, use the bulb syringe on the back of the throat; NEVER suction the nostrils before the throat. Syringing the nostrils first will cause the puppy to take a breath, inhaling fluids into the lungs. Be vigorous in your use of the syringe. Reach to the back of the throat and suction out the fluids. Then suction the nostrils. Suctioning the nostrils one time is usually enough. After each time that you have used up the suction of the bulb, pull it back out and empty it,

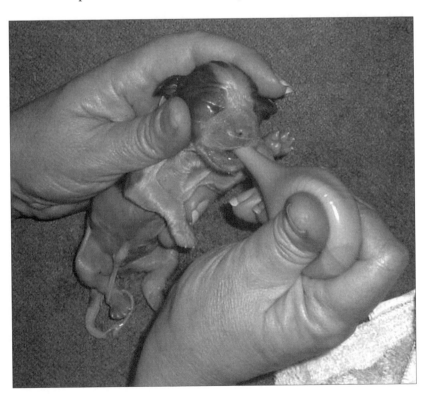

pressing the air out again onto one of the white washcloths to ready it for more suctioning. As long as you can see fluids being removed with the bulb syringe, it is doing its job and you can continue using it. Chances are very good that as the amount of fluid that you can see and remove decreases, the puppy will become pinker and have a more regular breathing pattern.

THE BREATH OF LIFE FOR YOUR PUPPY

If you have a puppy that is slow to breathe or "pink up" and you have suctioned him and re-suctioned him using the bulb syringe without success, don't give up. Try a little mouth-to-mouth resuscitation on him. Putting your mouth over the puppy's nose and mouth and making a tight seal, give the puppy a couple of very gentle puffs. Pull back and assess him. Repeat the two puffs. Gently massage the little chest while holding him in a head-down position. Holding him head-down will allow gravity to assist in getting the fluids out of his lungs. Assess the puppy again. Use the bulb syringe again. Give two puffs of air again. Keep changing the washcloth that you are holding him in so that you constantly have him in a warmed cloth to keep his body temperature up. You should have a good supply of warmed cloths in your warming box so that you can frequently change the cloths and keep the puppy warm. Work fast, repeating the steps of syringing, mouth-to-mouth and assessment.

SWINGING IS NOT FOR NEWBORNS

Do not "swing" the puppy. Many breeders have been using the old swinging technique for years. There are even videos that teach you how to swing your puppy. I realize that most books say that the canine newborn does not suffer the same type of brain damage from swinging that a human baby would suffer, but my response to this is that we don't have IQ tests for dogs. We have no way to assess the damage that might have been done to the puppy by swinging him. My thought is that the dog who took forever to housetrain, or was never able to learn how to roll over, could very well have been a puppy who was swung.

OXYGEN CAN HELP

Once the puppy is gasping, put him in the warming box and continue to use your oxygen in a "blow-by" method at 1–2 liters per minute (discussed in detail in Chapter 10). Ask your vet to give you a prescription for Dopram® and instruct you in its use prior to the whelping. It will often stimulate a puppy to start breathing. Be sure to use the bulb syringe to remove any loose secretions BEFORE you use the Dopram or the puppy could very well end up aspirating (inhaling) secretions.

If I could give you one single thing, I would give you confidence. I would wish for you to have the confidence to work fearlessly and tirelessly toward saving your puppy. Work hard, but always with the knowledge that you may well fail and the hope that you will succeed.

5

LET'S DO THE CORD CARE

NO GNAWING OR CHEWING ALLOWED!!

If you get really lucky, mom will deliver the puppy, lick off the amniotic sack, neatly chew the cord and proceed to stimulate the baby while you eat potato chips and watch TV. She might even housetrain him for you! In the real world however all moms are different, and yours might need some assistance, particularly if she is a first-time mom. Be prepared to assist with cord care.

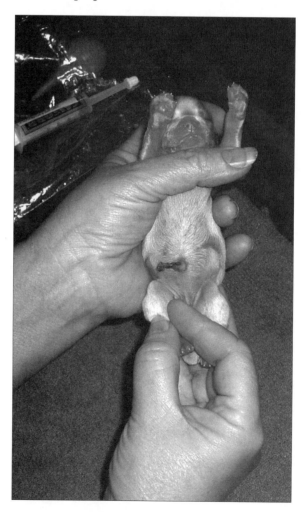

According to the books, cord care is best done by the mom who uses a chewing, gnawing action that will seal off the vessels in the umbilical cord. Now, I'm really willing to go the extra mile for my dogs. I don't mind picking up their poop, brushing their teeth or trimming their toenails. I'm a give, give, give kind of gal. HOWEVER, I draw the line at chewing on the cord. My advice to you is to purchase a nice pair of surgical scissors, some dental floss and some Betadine® solution and keep it all in a zip-close plastic bag stored in the warming box between puppy litters.

HELPING MOM WITH CORD CARE

Some moms really get energetic about the cord-chewing thing and simply won't leave it alone until she has eviscerated the puppy. You experienced breeders out there know what I'm talking about don't you? Watch her carefully and if you think that she is getting a tad on the compulsive side, take the puppy from her, move him to the warming box and take care of the cord yourself.

First, hold the placenta up off the puppy and, by using a "milking" kind of action, strip the blood in the cord down toward the puppy. Cord blood contains stem cells that are very beneficial to the puppy. These can assist the immune system. Tie off the cord as close to the body as possible with dental floss and then cut it with the scissors. Leave a stump of about an inch or so. Using a cotton-tipped swab or a cotton ball, dab some Betadine solution on the cord stump. The remainder of the cord will dry very quickly and fall off in a day or so. Remember that the germ-killing action of Betadine takes place while the Betadine is drying, so leave the baby in the warming box at least long enough for the Betadine to dry.

Keep in mind at all times that the cord stump is an open area on the skin and, because of that, acts as a welcome mat and open highway for little organisms that shouldn't be there. Keep your eye on the cord stump until it is completely dry. If it looks pink around the edges or stays moist for more than a day or so, there might be a problem. Smell the cord stump area. Infection has an unpleasant odor somewhat like spoiled meat. Once you actually "smell" infection, you will never forget it. If in doubt, put a little Betadine on it from time to time. It can't hurt and it might possibly head off an infection.

TWO TYPES OF UMBILICAL HERNIAS

As long as we are on the subject of umbilical cords, let's discuss umbilical hernias. From what I have been able to read and research, the thought is that true umbilical hernias are inherited. The important terms for you to learn are "reducible" and "non-reducible". Reducible hernias require surgery, non-reducible hernias do not. The most common form of an umbilical hernia is *not* reducible and therefore doesn't require surgery. If the hernia is a non-reducible hernia, the little ball of tissue on the tummy can't be pushed back, or reduced, into the abdomen. It feels firm to the touch and can basically only be moved around a little bit within the skin. With this that type of hernia the muscle wall closed over while the puppy was still quite young, trapping a small piece of fatty tissue outside of the muscle. It will feel very firm to the touch and the muscle under the small piece of firm tissue will be intact. This type of hernia is really quite harmless. The muscle wall after all, is intact, closed and firm. If you choose to repair it surgically, the surgery should be a very inexpensive one, with a very short recovery time — but it really isn't necessary other than for cosmetic reasons. This type of hernia will be evident by six weeks or so, if not sooner.

A hernia that is reducible is a true umbilical hernia and therefore will require surgery. When you push on the small piece of tissue at the umbilical cord site, your finger will easily go into the abdomen. You have been able to "reduce" the hernia's size by pushing it back into the abdomen. The feeling is unmistakable. You will feel as if your fingertip could easily reach all the way up and touch the spine. The little lump of tissue is extremely soft and if you put a stethoscope to it you will be able to hear bowel sounds. The reason that you can hear bowel sounds is because the small soft tissue that is protruding from the abdomen is actually a small piece of the bowel. This type of hernia *must be repaired*. What may eventually happen is the little loop of bowel may become entrapped in the skin and the tissues immediately under the skin (fascia tissue) become infected and necrotic or gangrenous. It will not heal on its own. It will require surgery. If it becomes entrapped, or "strangulated," it is life threatening and requires emergency care.

Just remember that you need to assess the hernia as the puppy grows. As long as the muscle wall closes, and the muscle feels firm and whole under the skin, the hernia is not the dangerous type. If you can reduce the hernia by pushing it up into the abdomen with ease, it will need repair.

6

COLOSTRUM...
WHAT IS IT?

IT IS THE IMMUNE SYSTEM OF YOUR PUPPY

The fact that your bitch produces colostrum and your puppy needs it is not exactly a brand new concept introduced to you here, for the very first time, on these pages. Colostrum is not "new news". However, no book on puppy care would be complete without a section on colostrum and ideally, there will be something here that you have not heard before.

Colostrum is present in the breast before the milk comes in. It is similar to milk but has a different chemical and molecular structure. It contains important life-saving antibodies and nutrients that stimulate the synthesis of protein. It increases the utilization of fat, promotes cell growth and supports the immune system. All of mom's immunities will be passed to her puppies in her colostrum. The effects will be there to protect the puppy for several weeks after birth. In the books I've researched, there seems to be a slight difference of opinion about when colostrum should be ingested to provide maximum protection. Some sources say within the first 12 hours and some say within the first 24 hours. After 24 hours of age, all the sources are all in agreement that it is either less effective or not effective at all.

Generally speaking, your puppy must have colostrum or an acceptable substitution in order to live. I am sure there are many times when a puppy has lived to a ripe old age without ever having had colostrum, but speaking in broad, general terms, the puppy must have it in order to survive. Pups who do not receive colostrum will not die immediately, but by seven days or so, they may begin to succumb to simple infections that could have been prevented by the ingestion of colostrum.

I was unable to find statistics for the percentage of puppies who will die without colostrum, but I did find statistics on newborn foals. Eighty percent of newborn foals who fail to receive colostrum will die. Although I was unable to find statistics or articles about the death rate for human babies who do not receive colostrum, I was able to find several articles that describe the practice in some cultures of preventing a newborn baby from nursing from his mother for the first 2–3 days of life because the substance in the breast at that time is not milk. This is a common practice in third world countries that also, not surprisingly, have very high infant death rates.

Clearly, it is of utmost importance to see that your puppies ingest colostrum or a substitute within the first 12–24 hours of life or your loss rate will be huge. Without it, they are left without an immune system. If you are unable to provide a good substitute, discuss the possibility of very early vaccinations with your vet.

HAND STRIPPING COLOSTRUM

There are times when your puppies simply cannot get colostrum without some assistance. Sometimes they are born so prematurely that their suck reflex isn't present and they can't nurse from mom. Many vets and breeders recommend trying to "strip" colostrum from the mom's breast. The process of stripping, or extracting milk by hand from the breast is often quite difficult — sometimes impossible. Stripping colostrum requires a massaging, milking type of action. Remember back to when you've seen cows being milked? It's harder than it looks. Using moist packs on the mom might help the process, however, if you cannot remove at least 1 cc* per puppy for toy breeds to 4 ccs for larger breeds, do not try to replace the colostrum by this method. When I've tried it I was unable to get an adequate amount to meet the need. Also, remember that if the pups are premature, often the mother simply hasn't gotten in the milk, so stripping becomes an impossibility. Sometimes a bitch will die during the birth process and obviously, there will no way to get colostrum from her.

Any glitch in the system between lactating bitch and nursing puppy can keep the puppy from getting its immune system building colostrum. If the puppy can't get it on his own, you need to know where to get the substitutes that will save your puppies.

SUBSTITUTES FOR COLOSTRUM

The first method for giving the puppy a replacement for the mother's immunities would be to take the mom and the puppy to the vet. The vet can draw blood from the mother, spin it down to a clear serum

I'd like to clear up any confusion you may have about "cc" and "ml". 1 cc, or cubic centimeter is equal in volume to 1 milliliter or "ml", therefore the two terms are interchangeable.

and inject the serum into the intraperitoneal cavity (non-organ part of the abdominal cavity) of the puppy's abdomen. This will work as well as colostrum. Your vet will know the correct amount needed for your specific breed. The warming box is the ideal way to transport your pups for this purpose.

Another thing that can be done to replace colostrum and its life-giving benefits is to have purchased, in advance of the whelping, a product called Fresh-Frozen Plasma, or FFP, which can be ordered from a company called Hemopet (see Resources). The Hemopet people keep a colony of neutered and spayed, sequestered, protected greyhounds that have the universal canine blood type. They regularly donate blood, which is separated into the needed components. FFP contains immunities for all of the major things that pups might get such as parvo or distemper, but it also contains immunity against a large number of other diseasess. You can order the product and have it delivered the next day still frozen and ready to keep in your freezer. It has a shelf life of about five years if kept frozen. A tube of FFP contains approximately 10–12 ccs of Fresh-Frozen Plasma and is relatively inexpensive. For a toy litter, one or two tubes will be sufficient. For larger breeds, you would need to plan your order based on the information that the Hemopet people can give you. You will find that shipping the frozen product is the expensive part. It will cost as much to ship one tube of FFP as to ship twenty. Speak with other breeders in your area about sharing the cost of the shipping on the order and placing a collective order.

FFP is designed to be given orally by tube feeding and should be given within the first 12 hours of life in order to be the most effective. If for some reason, you are unable to give it orally within the first 12–24 hours, you may also administer it sub-cutaneously (discussed in Chapter 11) just as if you were giving an immunization on the neck, or intraperotoneally by your vet. For a toy dog, only 1 cc is required. For the larger breeds, 4 ccs is required. When you call Hemopet to place an order, they will tell you how much FFP you will need for your breed. In addition to the antibodies that it contains, it is rich in all plasma proteins, which will boost the pups' nutrients and clotting factors. Clotting factors are vitally important for those of us who remove dewclaws or dock tails. If you anticipate that your bitch will need a caesarian section, you can even purchase a supply of FFP for her in case she has excessive bleeding during her caesarian section. It can be thawed and administered intravenously in an emergency. It can also be used on "fading puppies".

The FFP will be shipped to you frozen in tubes. It must be thawed prior to use, but it should never be heated past about

100-degrees. Remember that this is a body fluid, which is normally kept at the body temperature of the dog (101–102 degrees). Therefore, if you heat it above the canine body temperature, you could easily destroy the contents. You can either use warm water after you have taken the temperature of the water, or carry it in your bra or pocket (handier for you guys) to allow it to thaw slowly. First, rub it between your hands to begin the thawing process. It will thaw much more quickly than you would think. Once it is thawed, just hold it next to your body until it has reached your own body temperature, then tube feed it as you would any other product designed for tube feeding. You can use the same tube and syringe for an entire litter with only minor adjustments on the measurement and markings of the tube. Don't worry about cross contamination from puppy to puppy as long as they are all healthy, newborn pups. Remember, they will bump each other off the nipples and take right over. They practice cross-contamination all day long and, as a rule, live to tell the tale for several years.

Several milk replacement products advertise that they contain colostrum. The catch is that the colostrum they are talking about is from cattle and cattle don't get parvo or distemper as dogs do. These products sound good in concept, but are probably pretty useless in actual practice. There are only three ways for you to get colostrum into your puppies, give them passive immunity and disease resistance and save their lives: 1) The real thing — colostrum from the bitch; 2) clear serum from the bitch's blood injected into the puppy; or 3) FFP ingested orally within the first 12–24 hours of life followed with one dose each day for the following two days — a total of three doses given over three days.

7

A NORMAL NEWBORN PUP

PINK AND TWITCHY, BLIND AND DEAF

Immediately after delivery the puppy will be somewhat dusky — blue from lack of oxygen — limp and wet. After a he takes a few breaths, he should begin to pink up, perk up and start getting some muscle tone. Once he is dry, he should start crawling around in the warming box crying and rooting for something to eat. His eyes and ears will be sealed.

He will have a strong suckling reflex. He will have the instinctive behavior to root in his search for food. Don't get overly worried if a puppy seems to root around looking for a nipple but appears to be clueless as to what he is supposed to do with it once he finds it. Some pups will latch on and begin nursing vigorously from the get go, while others may take a few hours to coordinate the efforts of crawling, rooting and suckling. If you place the normal newborn on his back, he will right himself immediately. To further test his reflexes tap him gently around his eyes and he should have a blink response even though his eyes are sealed.

The normal puppy will be twitchy and jerky almost all the time when he is asleep. His ears will twitch, his lips will move and his paws will shift around constantly. He will lie sprawled out on his tummy or sides with his head tucked toward his chest. The puppy should feel warm to the touch. Even though the normal pup is in almost constant motion, he should be quiet. He will cry when he is hungry, but will tire quickly and fall asleep. He will compete for the nipples with his siblings. His birth weight should double in 8-10 days.

NORMAL VITAL SIGNS:

- respiration rate on day of birth: 8–18 irregular breaths per minute
- after the first day: 15–35 irregular breaths per minute
- heart rate on day of birth: 120–150 beats per minute
- heart rate first two weeks: 180–220 beats per minute
- body temperature from 1–2 weeks: 94–97-degrees (rectally)

If the bitch is healthy and provides enough milk, the single most important thing that you can provide for the normal, healthy newborn puppy is warmth. Change their bedding twice a day and as you change their bedding, check each of them. They should feel warm, look pink, act twitchy and the area under the tails should be clean. They should be quiet, but never still. The puppy who is still is the topic of the next chapter.

THE ORPHANED PUPPY

There is no reason to assume that the orphaned puppy will be a sick puppy. They are often quite vigorous and healthy. Tube feeding is necessary for the orphaned newborn until he has grown enough and gotten strong enough to take a milk substitute from a baby bottle. Making the switch from tube feeding to bottle feeding relates to the size and strength of the pup, not the age. By 12 oz their mouths are usually large enough and their sucking ability is strong enough for the nipple on a bottle. A Playtex® or similar baby bottle is a good choice for feeding a puppy.

As long as you follow the same guidelines that you would for any puppy, you can successfully rear an orphaned puppy or litter. Along with the usual things such as feeding and keeping the babies warm, you will have to assume the task of helping the baby to pee and poop. The mom stimulates those activities by her licking. I just don't think I'm going to be able to talk you into assuming the licking behaviors of the moms, so we'll have to learn other techniques. It is easy to get the puppy to pee. Tap the genitals with a cotton ball and you will start the flow of urine. It is sometimes a bit more challenging to get the puppy to poop on command — sometimes simply because he is not ready to do so. There are a couple of different things that work pretty well. These work best if used a few minutes after feeding the puppy. Put some petroleum jelly on your fingertip and rub the rectal area. Keep baby wipes nearby to assist with the clean up duties. Another thing that helps at times is to hold the puppy's rear end under warm flowing water at your basin. Sometimes the light pressure of the running water stimulates the bowels to move and clean up is a snap. Warm and dry the pup in the warming box.

If you know for sure that the puppy has not had a bowel movement in several hours, you might try a very small enema. You should have some Colace® stool softener gel tabs in your supply kit. Colace is widely available in drug stores and sometimes grocery stores as well. Buy the 100 mg dosage. Open a gel cap into about 10 ccs of warmed Lactated Ringers solution. Using a feeding tube set-up, pull about 3–4 ccs for toys breeds, 9–10 ccs for larger breeds into the syringe, and clear out the air and bubbles. After putting a small amount of petroleum jelly on the tip end of the tube, insert the feeding tube into the rectum and push a few ccs of the warmed Lactated Ringers containing the stool softener into the puppy's rectum. Leave the tube in for a few seconds so that the liquid doesn't come out immediately. If the puppy continually appears to be getting constipated, add a few drops of dark Karo® syrup to the feeding formula.

8

A SICK
NEWBORN PUP

ALL YOUR ASSESSMENT SKILLS ARE NEEDED

A well puppy can become a sick puppy within hours. That is why you should be checking your puppies several times a day and looking them over every time you pass their pen. Often, a mother will push a chilled pup away. Sometimes this behavior is misinterpreted as being a sign that the mother knows that something is wrong with the puppy. Actually, she will often reject a chilled puppy because he "feels" unhealthy, not because he is unhealthy. Because he is cold, and won't root or nurse, she will reject him. Therefore, the first thing would be to make sure that the puppy is warm. Often warming him up is enough. A sick pup will often be separated from his littermates, but so will an otherwise healthy pup who has gotten cold.

A sick puppy will probably not be nursing. If he is trying to nurse, he may be too weak to actually be getting milk from the breast. He may be crying. You may see him nursing at times, but it takes a certain amount of strength to remove milk from the breast. Don't assume that because a puppy is nursing, he is getting milk. Assess him from head to toe. Weigh each puppy every day; twice daily if you are worried, and record the weights. I've included a Puppy Weight Chart at the back of the book. The sick puppy will feel somewhat cooler to the touch. He may be dusky in color. He will usually have his head extended, rather than flexed toward his chest. He will not be twitchy and engaged in that "active" kind of sleep that you will see exhibited by the normal newborn puppy. His legs will often be pulled in toward his body rather than sprawled out. Once you have determined that your puppy is not behaving normally, you need to act quickly and begin your assessment.

Q&As FOR ASSESSING THE PUPPY

Answer these questions to decide what needs to be done to save your puppy:

Is the puppy warm to the touch?

Pick him up. Feel him. Compare the feeling of his body warmth to that of his littermates. Take his temperature rectally. Feel inside his mouth. For some reason, a sick puppy will often have a very cool mouth even if his body feels normal. His body temperature should be around 95-degrees. Warm him slowly. You want to avoid warming too quickly because if the skin warms too quickly, it will begin the dilation of the surface vessels to cool without allowing the core temperature to warm to the correct temperature. Hold him next to your body for a while. If you have your warming box turned on and warmed up, wrap him in a washcloth or hand towel and allow him to warm there. You can also warm a puppy by placing him in an open plastic bag and submerging the bag containing the puppy into a 95-degree water bath. Don't wet the puppy, just hold the open bag containing the puppy in the warm water until his body temp is 95-degrees.

Does he have a suck reflex?

Put your fingertip into his mouth. A healthy puppy will have a strong suck reflex that you should be able to feel immediately.

Does he have good muscle tone?

Pull out his little legs. Do they pull right back into position? Is he limp in your hands or pulling himself into a little ball? If he is limp and his head is hanging, you are definitely holding a very sick pup. Prognosis: not good, but worth fighting for.

Is he breathing with his mouth open and gasping or closed?

Gasping is ALWAYS bad. Gasping is the puppy's reflex action to bring in as much oxygen as possible. A gasping puppy needs oxygen. No matter what else may be happening with him, the fact that he is gasping means that you need to oxygenate him. Oxygenation is covered in Chapter 10.

Does he appear to be dehydrated?

When you pull up the skin at the back of the neck, does it stay in a little "tent" or does it spring back quickly? You want it to spring back quickly. Keep in mind that this process of checking for elasticity (turgor) of the skin is, at best, a poor method of detection. Imagine trying to determine hydration by tenting the skin on a little Shar Pei puppy. A better way to assess hydration is by comparing him to his littermates. Does his skin appear to be more wrinkled than the other puppies? This wrinkling would be caused by decreased moisture in his tissues. Are his eyes more sunken into his head?

What is the color of his urine?

Take a clean, white cotton ball and tap his genitals. As you tap his genital area, it will stimulate him to void. Is the urine on the cotton ball a light straw color, or is it a darker yellow? Urine should be a light straw color. Dark urine is an indication of dehydration. Not being able to get urine on the cotton ball is a sign that either the bladder has recently been emptied or the puppy is more severely dehydrated. Try again in 20 minutes.

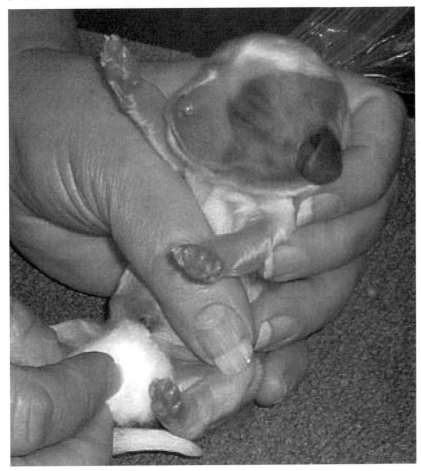

What is the specific gravity of the puppy's urine?

This is the way that specific gravity works: water has a specific gravity of 1.000, normal urine has a specific gravity of approximately 1.020, concentrated urine (a sign of dehydration) has a specific gravity of 1.030–1.040. The more "solid" parts there are in the urine when compared to the "liquid" parts of the urine, the more dehydrated the puppy is. How do you measure specific gravity of your puppy?

Easy. Be prepared prior to the delivery by purchasing the little sticks that you can use to do an analysis of the puppy's urine: DiaScreen Reagent Test Strips® (see Resources). Instead of tapping the genitals with the cotton ball if you suspect dehydration, tap the genitals with the portion of the strip that is for measuring specific gravity. If the specific gravity is in the 1.030–1.040, there is an excellent chance that your puppy is dehydrated.

Is the puppy crying for more than 15 minutes or so?

A crying puppy is not unusual unless the crying continues for more than 15 minutes. A normal puppy will tire by then and cry himself to sleep. Prolonged crying is in indication that the puppy is in distress. Listen carefully. The cry of a sick puppy will often have a different sound, an unusual tone, usually higher pitched. If all else seems to be okay with the puppy, but he continues to fuss and cry, you might use a few drops of Mylicon Drops® on the puppy's tongue to disburse any gas he may have trapped in his tummy.

Is he cuddled up to his littermates or off by himself?

If he is some distance away from the others, and every time you check the puppies, the same puppy is away from the others, it is time to assess the puppy for signs of illness.

Is the puppy moving around or lying quietly? Is he twitchy?

Remember that the normal, healthy puppy is in almost constant motion — little subtle twitches and jerks. A perfectly still puppy is a puppy with a problem.

Does the umbilical cord site look clean and dry?

It should be drying and falling off within a day or so at most. It shouldn't be reddened, nor should it have an odor. If it shows signs of infection: redness, swelling, discharge or a foul odor, call the vet immediately and follow her instructions. Just remember that if she puts the puppy on antibiotics, you will need to give him just a small amount of plain yogurt* every day to replace the normal flora and fauna of the intestinal tract that the antibiotics will remove. Just a small amount on the tip of your finger is fine. Let the puppy lick it

*Not all yogurts are created equal. Many have been heated thereby killing most of the friendly bacteria you are trying to put back into the puppy or the mom. Select one from a health food store or one that meets National Yogurt Association criteria for live and active culture yogurt.

off or place it on his tongue. If the bitch needs to go on antibiotics, same thing — small amounts of yogurt for the puppies and more for the mom.

Is stool caked around the rectal area of the puppy?
This is often a sign that the puppy has had diarrhea or that the mother has stopped cleaning him, both of which require further assessment.

Are the eyelids clean?
Even if the eyes are still closed, there can be discharge and drainage. Generally speaking, if one or both of the eyes open very early — say at 3–4 days of age — that is a puppy that will need to be observed very carefully. This isn't a good sign. Call your vet immediately and follow the instructions that you are given. These puppies often end up with "dry eye" and ulcerations of the eyes.

Are signs of infection present at other open areas?
Check any other open areas — dewclaw removals, tail dockings, etc. Check for the normal signs of infection: redness, swelling, discharge or a foul odor. Contact the vet immediately if there are signs and symptoms of infection. You will probably need to have the puppy on an antibiotic and yogurt. Follow the instructions of the vet for the administration of all medications.

Are the lips clean and dry or is there additional moisture there?
Often, a sick baby will have extra moisture around the lips. Sometimes just a clear drool, other times it is bubbly.

When the puppy breathes, are the respirations audible? Do his lungs sound crackly or moist? What is his respiration rate?
Remember that the first day, the respiration rate should be around 8–18 breaths per minute and for the first two weeks after that around 15–35. You can count them by watching the chest rise and fall. Don't worry if they are irregular. If the puppy has audible breaths and the lungs appear to be crackly, *and* there are other signs of illness, contact your vet immediately. A stethoscope will come in handy for this. The puppy may have pneumonia if his respirations are noisy. A word of caution here: whether the respiration rate is at the low end of normal, or the high end of normal — normal is exactly that — normal. After the puppy is a day old, anything between 15 and 35 irregular breaths per minute is normal. See Chapter 7 for more on respiration.

WHAT NEXT?

Now that you have assessed the puppy and you have begun to get a feel for what the problem may be, let's go back to our original premise that you are alone in the middle of the night on a holiday weekend with a raging snowstorm outside. What do you do now?

We all know that our first step would be to call our vet, but what do we do if our vet is unavailable, or we can't get to his or her office? What then? Do you sit by and watch your puppy die, or do you get aggressive and try to save your puppy? Do you assume that losing 30% of your pups is Mother Nature's way? Do you let your fear of procedures that are usually performed by trained medical personnel keep you from learning those skills? The decision is yours to make.

As you begin to work hard to save this puppy, take a deep breath and tell yourself that your chances of saving him are far from 100 percent. Don't expect that putting your puppy into intensive care is a guarantee that he will live. Go into it with the expectation that he will likely die and the hope that he will live. If our expectations are high every time, it gets to be too emotionally draining every time one of our pups dies. You can do nothing but your best for your puppies, but none of us are miracle workers — there will be puppies that will die no matter what we do. I lose puppies every year. There are puppies with problems that are simply not compatible with life. Sometimes the fight to save the puppy is really about knowing you've done your best. That puppy, in all likelihood, is here because you planned a breeding. Give him every chance for life, and try to let the fact that you did your best be your emotional reward; not saving the puppy, but knowing you did your best.

Warming the puppy

If your puppy is cold, warm him up. DO NOT FEED A COLD PUPPY UNDER ANY CIRCUMSTANCES. The peristaltic action of the intestines will completely stop if the puppy gets chilled. Food will sit in the stomach indefinitely and will not move into the small intestine. It may sour and cause the pup to vomit, which puts him at further risk for aspiration pneumonia. The first step is to warm him. Warm him slowly so that you avoid the rebound action of rapid warming that we discussed before. If the skin warms too rapidly, the surface vessels will dilate in an attempt to cool the body. The core temperature, however, will remain low. So the key is to warm him slowly. Skin to skin contact with your body is perfect, but you can also wrap him in a warmed washcloth and allow him to warm in the warming box. A sports bra is ideal for warming a small puppy, but I'm not too sure that you men who breed dogs will have a good fit handy.

Hydrating the puppy

If the sick puppy appears to be a little dehydrated, assess to see if it appears as if he has had diarrhea. If so, consider hydrating him using the sub-cutaneous method detailed in Chapter 10. Be sure that the fluid is warm but no higher than 95-degrees. An easy way to warm the fluid is to carry the filled syringe in your bra or next to your skin for a while, or to drop it into a small bowl of warm water. Check the temperature of the water with your thermometer. You'll be surprised at how "cool" 95-degrees can feel. I like to use a fluid containing water and electrolytes (and in some formulas, glucose) such as Lactated Ringers, but your vet may prefer that you use only normal saline. Follow the advice of your particular vet, keeping in mind that the brain metabolizes ONLY glucose, so if hydration has to go on for a lengthy period of time, you may want to inquire about using a solution that also contains glucose. Watching a puppy "come back to life" after a warm infusion of sub-cutaneous fluids is really rather dramatic. IV solutions are available from pet supply catalogs (see Resources) but will require a prescription from your vet. One liter comes with my Puppy Intensive Care Warming Box. Once you have used it, keep it refrigerated, and it should be good for about one year.

Tube feeding the puppy

If the sick puppy doesn't appear to have had diarrhea, tube feed him. If his dehydration appears to be fairly serious, combine the two methods. Tube feed him a warm feeding with a milk substitute made for puppies and use the IV fluids to hydrate him sub-cutaneously. Weigh him and translate the ounces into ccs and you will have the right amount: a puppy weighing 6 oz needs to be tube fed 6 ccs. Do the same with the sub-cutaneous fluid replacement — 1 cc fluid for every ounce of weight. You can repeat that in two hours if he is still dehydrated. Tap his genitals with a clean white cotton ball after every feeding to assess his state of dehydration. If the urine is dark or if you are unable to get urine, then continue hydrating him until his urine is a light straw color. Use your DiaScreen Test Strips® from time to time as another assessment tool to see if the puppy is dehydrated. If the urine is colorless, back off on the amount of fluid/food you are giving him. Colorless urine is in indication of more than adequate hydration.

Oxygen for the puppy

If he is gasping, or if his respiration rate is less than the low end of normal or more than the high end of normal, give him oxygen. Chapter 10 will explain in detail how to do this.

Stopping diarrhea

If he has had diarrhea, give him some baby strength Kaeopectate®, about 3–5 ccs, along with some plain yogurt. You can dilute this with some Pedialyte® and give it by the feeding tube. You can repeat this after every bout of diarrhea. Kaeopectate is clay based and is designed to absorb fluids and stabilize the intestinal tract. It isn't a medication that will get into his system. The yogurt will replace good bacteria in the intestines. Remember that until you fix the diarrhea, you will need to hydrate the puppy using the sub-cutaneous method because everything you put into his intestinal tract will just come right back out again, taking valuable electrolytes with it. The general rule of thumb for a puppy who has diarrhea or vomiting is to keep him "NPO," which means to give nothing by mouth, other than some Kaeopectate. Consult with your vet as soon as possible when a puppy has diarrhea for his/her guidance for how long to proceed with the care of this puppy and when to resume tube feedings.

Stopping an infection

In case he has an infection, it wouldn't hurt to keep the antibiotic Keflex® in your medicine chest (also available as aquarium medication from the pet catalogs without a prescription). If you are unable to get to your vet, call her and describe the symptoms that you are seeing. She can help you decide the dose and how to prepare the antibiotic. In an emergency, you can open a capsule and mix it in yogurt or even in your formula for tube feeding.

The good news is as long as you are watchful, continue your assessments and keep in contact with the vet, you should be able to treat your puppy.

IMPORTANT THINGS TO REMEMBER

The things that will kill your puppy, other than a birth defect that is not compatible with life, are:

- being too cold or too warm
- getting dehydrated
- having low blood sugar

- having an infection
- not getting enough oxygen

Many of these things are "fixable" within your puppy intensive care unit and once you have learned the steps for assessment, the actions you take are really quite simple:
- warm the puppy
- hydrate the puppy (include glucose)
- oxygenate the puppy
- treat for diarrhea if present
- treat for infection if present

Memorize these steps and someday you will save a puppy that you might otherwise have lost.

As you assess your puppy from head to toe, from system to system, take notes and write down your findings. When you are finally able to reach your vet, he or she will need to know:
- puppy's temperature
- respiration rate
- hydration status
- color of his urine
- weight and weight loss
- the sounds that he makes as he breathes.

Your vet will appreciate the information that you have gathered and can use it to help make a diagnosis.

9

THE CHILLED PUPPY

JUST DON'T LET IT HAPPEN

The temperature of a newborn puppy should be just about 94–96-degrees. The puppy's internal thermostat doesn't start working until the puppy is about 3 weeks old, so if you think about it, the 95-degree mark makes sense. The mom's temperature is about 101–102-degrees and if the puppy snuggles up to the mom's body, he should be able to keep his own temp at about 95-degrees from the heat he will get from her body. By two weeks, he is supposed to be 97–99-degrees and by this time, the puppies have learned to climb between her front legs, back legs and up under the neck. They've begun to be strong enough to get in closer to her for additional warmth. By three weeks of age, a normal puppy should be able to maintain his body heat with only minimal support from you or mom.

KEEPING MOM AND PUPPIES WARM

This is a good place to remind you that your warming box can be viewed as an incubator in a nursery. It isn't large enough for the mom and is intended for use as you care for your puppies only. Don't confuse it with a whelping box, or a puppy pen. After the delivery process, some breeders leave mom and babies in the large whelping box where mom delivered her pups, and others move them to a puppy pen. The size of your breed will influence your choice. There are many techniques and systems in use all over the world for keeping a litter of puppies warmed. They range from heating pads, to heat lamps, to increasing the ambient temperature in the room to sophisticated electronic sensors. Coming from a background of labor and delivery and neonatal intensive care where I had the most sophisticated equipment at my fingertips, of course I gravitated immediately to the best that was available to me. I use the Heated Whelping Nest® (see Resources) which has a sensor device that senses the temperature of the pups' bodies. If the pups' temp goes down to 94-degrees, it clicks on, and if it goes above 96-degrees, it clicks off. After their birth I move my Cavaliers to a 36"x36" puppy pen with a wooden floor that has been constructed to fit the inside the pen. The plywood is covered with linoleum to allow for easy cleaning and disinfecting. The whelping nest is about 20 inches across and fits neatly into the linoleum-covered plywood floor that is sitting on pieces of 2x4s. I cover the Whelping Nest with a single puppy pad, (contrary to manufacturer's instruction) and change the pad as necessary to keep the area clean. The manufacturer of the Heated Whelping Nest recommends leaving the puppies on the black plastic surface, but I have found that the addition of a single puppy pad on the floor of the puppy pen does not affect its ability to keep the puppies warm. My puppies just love this set up and have never wandered off their heat source. I also cover the entire puppy pen with a fitted quilt cover to give mom the illusion of being in her own little "den" and to give the new moms and their babies as much privacy as possible.

If you have puppies that are wandering away from their heat source into the corner of the puppy pen and crying until you retrieve them, the system you are using is in need of revision. What is happening is that they are getting too warm, leaving the area to cool off and not being able to find their way back to the warmed area. They cry when they become too cold. You are putting the puppies at some risk because by allowing their body temperature to fluctuate. The noses should be pink, but if there is too much redness, the puppy is overheated. If the body becomes overheated, his body will make an effort to cool itself by dilation of the surface vessels to expose more blood to the air to cool down. The same thing happens to us if we become overheated. That's why we become flushed as our body temperature rises.

Check the temperature of your warmed area by taking a regular glass thermometer, covering it with a folded hand towel and leaving it in place for about 20 minutes or so. If it goes above 95-degrees, you are providing too much warmth for the puppy. If it is below 94-degrees, you are not providing enough warmth for your puppies. Hundreds of puppies have survived being too warm and being too cool, but why subject the puppy to that stress if you know how to prevent it, and if the equipment to prevent it is available to you?

If a puppy becomes chilled, a variety of things begin to happen. He loses his suck reflex, his intestinal system begins to close down, and his stomach will not push food forward into the small intestine for digestion. DON'T FEED A COLD PUPPY. The chilled body will go into a sort of suspended animation. If the puppy has a core temperature of 70-degrees (approximately room temperature), you will probably not be able to tell if he is alive or dead. About the only reflex he will have left at that point is the natural reflex to spread his legs when dropped. This may sound rather cruel, and you may be reluctant to try it, but it is one of the only ways to assess if the puppy is dead or alive. Hold the puppy about 6 inches away from the heated surface of your warming box and *drop him on his tummy.* If the puppy spreads out his legs and then quickly pulls them back in, he is still alive.

Even puppies which have had no audible heartbeat have been revived after 15–30 minutes of stimulation and warming. Wrap the puppy in warmed washcloths or towels and keep him in the warming box. Keep rubbing and stimulating the puppy. Don't make the final decision about whether or not the puppy is dead or alive until the puppy is warm and still acting "dead." If he doesn't react to the "drop test" when he is warm to the touch, he is dead.

Emergency Room staff have a saying about victims of drowning in cold water or being left in cold weather: *"It's not dead until it's warm and dead."* This is a concept that you should keep in mind when you are caring for a chilled puppy. Check the puppy frequently while he is warming up. You can oxygenate him as well as described in Chapter 10. Once the puppy is warm, check his reflexes again. Tap around the eye sockets. Even if his eyes are sealed, he will still have a blink reflex. Put your fingertip in the mouth to check the suck reflex. Administer mouth to mouth by covering his mouth and nostrils and giving a couple of gentle puffs into his lungs. If there are signs of life, don't give up until you are sure he is gone.

10

SOMETIMES GASSY IS GOOD

AHHHH...OXYGEN. THE GAS OF THE GODS

It is a common misconception that oxygen and the tools necessary to administer it are available to you only by prescription from your vet. This is untrue. If you know where to go to find all of the pieces, oxygen is available to you as a layperson. If you know how to use it, you can save the life of your puppy. So...are you ready to get gassy?

Oxygen is a life saver. There is simply no other way to say it. It is safe, easy to obtain, and inexpensive. Sometimes puppies come out crying, crawling around and "pinking up" immediately. Other times, they are dusky (bluish in color), lethargic, limp, gasping and in need of more help. The help they need at this time is oxygen. If you have prepared in advance of the delivery, you will be ready to administer oxygen if you determine that your puppy can use it. Try out your tank and regulator well before delivery so that you are confident and can begin using the oxygen immediately. Have it set up as soon as mom goes into labor. Here are the guidelines that tell you that your puppy needs oxygen:

- Puppy is dusky, or blue
- Puppy is gasping for air
- Puppy is limp, but alive
- Puppy is lethargic, not moving around
- Puppy was gurgling with a lot of secretions in his mouth and throat at birth, but has now been suctioned out; use a little oxygen to compensate for the suctioning.

OXYGEN TANKS

Oxygen tanks are available to you from welding shops. They are not supposed to sell oxygen to you for any purposes other than commercial welding use. Knowing that, it probably isn't a good idea to go marching into the welding shop with a sick, gasping puppy yelling, "Help me! My puppy is dying!" Better to go well in advance of the whelping date and ask to buy a small canister of oxygen and make sure it is refillable. Become a welder for a day. A small canister of oxygen costs about $60.00 in my area, but prices may vary depending on where you live. My canister is 13 inches high and 16 inches in circumference.

The oxygen sold at welding shops is identical to that used for medicinal purposes. The tanks are usually, but not always, green. Maybe only some part of the tank will be green. They are packed under great pressure. Store the oxygen with the tank on its side because if kept upright, it is at a greater risk of being tipped over and possibly damaging the regulator or the apparatus for turning it off and on. If the top comes off in a fall, it can be quite dangerous. Leave it on its side at all times when you are using it and remember it is very flammable. Carry it in the trunk of your car, secured in a box to avoid it rolling around. When oxygen is packed into the canisters, it is measured in pounds per square inch or psi. You will need an oxygen regulator to convert the measurements of psi into liters per minute which is the flow rate used for medical purposes.

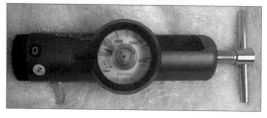

OXYGEN REGULATORS

Be careful that you buy a regulator for medical purposes and not for welding. A regulator for welding is NOT SAFE for your purposes. The tanks that you get at the welding store will almost always have a screw-on feature. It will look like the watering end of a yard hose. The regulator that you will need is of the "threaded" variety. Another name for this type of regulator is the "nut" variety. It must have the apparatus needed to screw on to the tank. If you purchase my Deluxe Puppy Intensive Care Warming Box you will get the correct regulator, tubing and connectors.

In the previous photo, the regulator attached to the oxygen tank with the screw-on or "nut" end is the *correct* kind. Regulators that have a T shaped screw to attach to the tank are the *incorrect* kind of regulator. It is easy recognize these. Unfortunately for all of us, the ones we *don't* need are by far the most common ones available. If you purchase this item on your own, here are some useful how-to's: go to eBay® or other auction site, type in "oxygen regulator," looking for the screw-on variety and bid on one. It will usually be described as being for "medical use." If in doubt, e-mail the person who is selling the regulator before you place a bid and ask if it is for medical use. Run like the wind from the T screw variety because it will not work with the tank you are getting from the welding store. Regulators come in all shapes, colors and sizes and a range of prices. If in doubt, send me a link to the image of the one you are interested in, myrasavant@hotmail.com, prior to bidding on it, and I can usually (but not always) tell you if it is the type you need.

Now that you have your tank and your regulator, you need oxygen tubing. If you're purchasing this item on your own, just stay put there right on the auction site and type in "oxygen tubing" and bid on some of that as well. Even though at first glance the tubing appears to be the same type of tubing that people use in aquariums, you need actual oxygen tubing in order to have the correct connector that will fit on the regulator. Oxygen tubing is part of my Puppy Intensive Care Warming Box. Now you are ready to administer oxygen to your puppies if they need it.

ADMINISTERING OXYGEN

There are basically three ways to administer oxygen to the puppy:

- by the "blow-by" method
- by mask
- by hood

Blow-by is the simplest method and can even be used very casually for a normal newborn litter just to give their oxygen levels a little boost. You just hold the end of the tubing about ½" from the mouth and nose and let them inhale it for a while. You can run blow-by oxygen at 0.5 to 2 liters per minute. 1 liter per minute is usually quite sufficient. Once the puppies are nice and pink and active, there is no longer a use for oxygen.

Giving oxygen by mask is for a puppy that may need a little bit more help. If the puppy is relatively quiet and still, you can make a small mask using a 3 oz paper cup for a toy breed or a 5 oz paper cup for other breeds. Simply make a small hole in the bottom of the cup next to the edge and insert the tubing into the cup and put the cup over the pup's nose and mouth as shown. Secure the tubing with some tape and you will have a makeshift oxygen mask. You can run oxygen by mask at 0.5 to 2 liters per minute; again, 1 liter per minute is usually quite sufficient.

Giving oxygen using a hood is for long-term usage. If you have a pup that might need prolonged exposure to oxygen, use a hood. The hood is easy to construct using a plastic cake cover that usually comes on cakes from the grocery store. Pick a cake that you really like, because if your puppy is sick enough to need a hood, you're going to be up with him at least every two hours while you are working night shift in the Puppy Intensive Care Unit. You can at least enjoy having a piece of cake from time to time. Cut a small hole in the top of the hood for venting and a small hole at the bottom along the side for the tubing and place the tubing next to the puppy and cover the puppy with the hood allowing the tubing to come out the hole that you have cut along the bottom edge. Run oxygen in the hood at 1 to 2 liters per minute.

The rate at which you run the oxygen is going to have to be determined by you. Base your decision on the color of the puppy. Look at the nose, pull down the eyelid and look at the color of those tissues, open the mouth and check the color of the gums. If the puppy looks normal to you at 0.5 to 1 liter per minute, then leave it at 0.5 to 1 liter per minute. Normal means, pink nose, pink inner eyelids, and nice pink gums. Compare him to his siblings. The normal respiration rate for a newborn is 8-18 breaths per minute and the breaths are often irregular. If in doubt, count the breaths. If the puppy appears still slightly dusky at 1 liter per minute, or if the pup is breathing with a gasping kind of action, increase the oxygen to 2 liters per minute.

Oxygen should never be run at the highest levels that your regulator is capable of reaching. There are two reasons for this — both are very good ones: 1) The drive to breathe is caused by the need for oxygen saturation of the blood. If you administer oxygen at a level that is too high, you will decrease the natural drive of the puppy to breathe. You want to *supplement* the oxygen, but you don't want to *flood* the system with oxygen; 2) Oxygen at too high a level can cause blindness because of retinal damage. You are safe at 0.5 to 2 liters per minute. I wouldn't advise going above 2 liters per minute without specific instructions from your vet.

Oxygen is *extremely* flammable. For this reason, never use it around an open flame, including stoves, candles, or cigarettes. Never use oil products around the canister, the regulator or the tubing. This includes petroleum jelly products. Oil products will only increase the flammability of oxygen. If you are using oxygen while the puppy is in the warming box, place the heating pad UNDER the warming box rather than inside it. This will avoid the risk of fire. Those candle lit dinners that you were preparing to eat while administering oxygen to your puppy are definitely out.

Room air consists of about 21% oxygen. The rest of the air you breathe is composed of other gases. Oxygen, which is run at 1 liter per minute, is just about the same percentage of oxygen as room air. Oxygen, which is run at 2 liters per minute, is about 25% oxygen.

Oxygen at 3 liters per minute is approximately 28% oxygen. You can see by these percentages, that the administration of oxygen to your puppy described here is safe. In conclusion, if your puppy is gasping, or if his color is "off," dusky and blue instead of pink, feel confident in giving him some supplemental oxygen. Oxygen is synonymous with "strength and endurance" and will not hurt your puppy.

11

THE DEHYDRATED PUPPY

TUBE FEEDING AND SUB-CUTANEOUS HYDRATION

A puppy can become dehydrated very quickly. It happens for a variety of reasons. No matter what the reason is, it must be fixed quickly or your puppy will die. If the puppy's fluid volume is significantly decreased, the heart is affected and the kidneys can be damaged. If you are unable to get the puppy to nurse enough from the mom to fix the problem you will need to hydrate the puppy. A good rule of thumb is: smaller or weaker pups who are full term should be fed or hydrated every 3 to 4 hours. Larger and/or older pups can manage being fed or hydrated every 8 hours. If the puppy isn't gaining weight, you will need to increase either the amount of hydration/feeding per feeding or hydrate/feed more often. Weigh the puppy every day and keep a record on the record chart at the back of the book.

Sometimes all that is necessary is to hydrate the pup, warm him, give him some time to regroup and he will be ready to go back in with the mom. Other times, you will need to take the puppy from the mom and keep him in the warming box, checking the temperature of the warming box and the puppy often to make sure he does not become overheated.

There are two ways that you can re-hydrate the puppy: you can feed him by tube feeding or you can inject fluid into the tissues immediately under the skin. In other words, you can use either oral hydration techniques, sub-cutaneous techniques, or a combination of the two. The choice between the two is simple. If the puppy has diarrhea or is vomiting, you will need to use sub-cutaneous hydration techniques. Do not tube feed a puppy with diarrhea or one who is vomiting. If the puppy does not have diarrhea, use a prepared formula to tube feed him. If he has diarrhea, administer fluids sub-cutaneously to keep him hydrated and keep his electrolytes in good balance. If your puppy does not appear to have diarrhea and is severely dehydrated, you can use both techniques at the same time until your puppy is well hydrated.

ORAL HYDRATION BY TUBE FEEDING

For the puppy that is not vomiting and does not have diarrhea, tube feeding him is your first choice. If you are uncertain if he is experiencing diarrhea, separate him from his mom and keep him in the warming box for an hour or so. Sometimes the moms clean them up so quickly, that it is difficult to know if the pup has diarrhea or not unless you get the puppy away from the mom for a while.

When it comes to oral hydration I *never* advocate the use of an eyedropper or baby bottle on a dehydrated puppy. More of the liquid will end up ON the puppy than IN the puppy, and the puppy is much more likely to inhale fluids (aspirate) than with the other methods. Aspiration pneumonia is often fatal, so feeding with an eyedropper or a bottle is truly not a good choice for supplementing the fluid needs of the pup. Bottle-feeding will work on an older puppy with a strong suck reflex, but if that puppy had a strong suck reflex, chances are pretty good he wouldn't have gotten dehydrated in the first place. So you are going to have to view tube feeding as the first choice for oral hydration of a puppy that does not have diarrhea.

Tube feeding seems to frighten many people. There are even articles on the internet that tell you how dangerous tube feeding is. I've got news for those people. Tube feeding has been around for a long, long time. It is the safest of all the artificial means of oral hydration. It delivers the correct amount of fluid, to the right place, in the least amount of time and in the safest possible manner. In addition, it will allow for hydration using Pedialyte, protein feedings or a combination of the two. Baby foods can be thinned and fed by tube and medications can be given by tube.

It is easy to learn how to tube feed. Once you have done it two or three times, your hands will stop shaking and you will no longer be convinced that you are killing the puppy with every feeding. Everybody is afraid the first few times they tube feed a puppy. Everybody. Although I have tube fed infants who weighed 2–3 pounds for years, the first time I tube fed a puppy who weighed 3 oz, I was absolutely terrified and certain that I would kill my puppy. What convinced me to go ahead and do it was that I knew for a certainty that he would die without it. You may feel terrified too. Actually, you should be prepared for this feeling of terror if you've never done it before. You're in good company. We all feel the same way. The key is just to get busy and do the feeding. Learning how to tube feed is a skill you will appreciate having for years to come.

Equipment needed

See the Resources for supplier information for the components. If it comes in my Puppy Intensive Care Warming Box I've put a * next to the item:

- Feeding tubes*. A size 8 French feeding tube is great for a pup up to 8 ounces. For a pup weighing a pound and a half or so, a size 10 French tube is fine. There are red tubes available and also clear silicone tubes. Either will work well, and they are interchangeable. Buy tubes that are about 40 centimeters long (15") from a company selling human pediatric feeding tubes and supplies (see Resources).

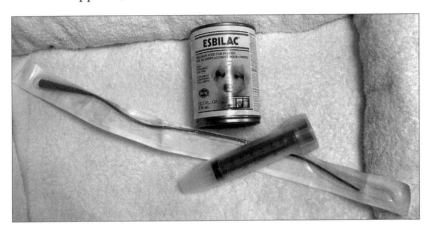

- Syringes* must be designed to fit the end of your feeding tube. Some feeding tubes require a syringe that screws into the end of the tube. This is called a Luer Lock syringe and tube. Some require the sort of syringe that is tapered and simply fits snugly inside the tube. This is usually referred to as the "slip" type of set up. Choose your syringe based on what type of tube you have. The same companies that sell the tubes will sell you the syringes.
- A felt-tipped marking pen.
- A food source such as Esbilac, Just Born® or goat's milk. I prefer Esbilac pre-mixed and sold in cans, but experienced breeders reading this will have their own preferences. Just in case you badly need a food source and you don't have a supply of your preferred type before the whelping date, here is a makeshift formula recipe until you are able to get something that you are used to using. It will last two days in your refrigerator, but after that, re-mix it from scratch. Start with one cup of whole milk. Add one teaspoon of regular vegetable oil, any type. Put in one drop of a liquid multivitamin for infants, widely available at drug stores, and two egg yolks. Blend it up.

- There are several ways to warm your food source. You can use the microwave for just a few seconds, keep the filled tube in the warming box for a while under the bumpered pad or carry it next to your body perhaps tucked in a bra or a pocket near your body. Don't feed it right out of the refrigerator and don't feed it too hot. Remember what the puppy's body temperature is supposed to be at that age (see Chapter 9) and don't go over that temperature.
- A clean, well lit surface. The warming box* works well on a kitchen counter. I sit at the breakfast bar as I tube feed the puppies. As usual, I use the warming box as my work surface.

Measure the tube

Lay the puppy on his side on a clean, covered surface. Find the last rib. The level of the last rib is the approximate level of the stomach. Hold the tube at the level of the last rib and just place it alongside the puppy until you get it to the level of the mouth. Just imagine where his esophagus would be and lay it along the side of the body following that pathway. Mark it with the marking pen right at the level of the lips. In addition to the photos here, the DVD that comes with this book shows you how to it. Practice the measuring technique on your next litter or even on a little stuffed dog. If the tube is inserted

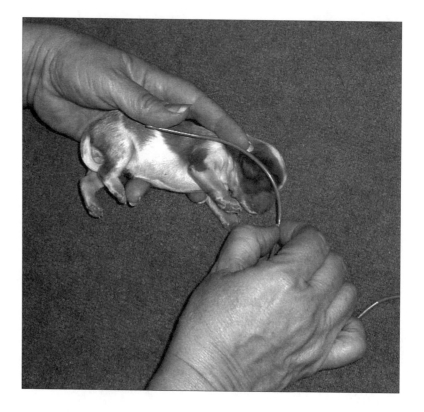

so that the mark you made is even with the lips, the tube will be in the right place.

Insert the tube

Now, for the scary part — the insertion of the tube. Holding the puppy in your non-dominant hand (in my case my left hand, as I am right handed) insert the tube into the puppy's mouth using your dominant hand. The puppy will fight you unless he is near death but he will show the most resistance as you get to the back of the throat. That is where his gag and swallow reflexes are located. It is uncomfortable for him when the end of the tube hits those areas. Just push past the resistance at the back of the throat and *keep pushing the tube in until the mark you made on the tube is right at the level of his lips.*

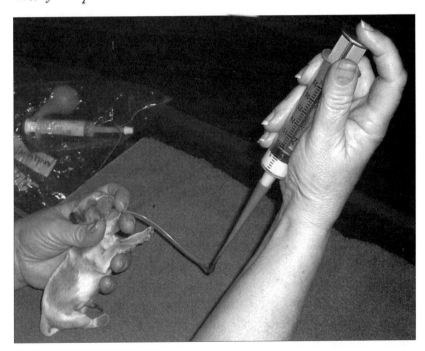

Then, hold the tube in place — don't let it slip back out. Watch the DVD to see how you can hold it in place using your first two fingers. Syringe in the food/fluid source with the syringe held above the puppy's head. Push the syringe in slowly, not forcefully, but also not so slowly that you are only prolonging the puppy's discomfort. If milk comes up out of the nose, you are feeding the puppy too quickly. If the puppy is crying, all the better, because as long as he is crying, you can rest assured that the tube isn't in his lung. The trachea, which leads to the lung, will end at about the level of the puppy's elbow. If you get the tube into the trachea, the puppy will be turning blue because you have occluded his airway. He will be unable to cry and you will be unable to pass the tube further than about the level of the elbow. If you think the tube has gotten into the trachea, pull it out as fast as you can, and give the puppy a 5-minute rest before you try again.

Amounts to feed

Consult with your vet and follow his instructions. However, if you are unable to reach your vet, you are safe going with this concept: your puppy will need approximately 30 ccs of liquid food source and/or Pedialyte for every 4 ounces of body weight per day. In other words, if your puppy weighs 8 ounces, you will need to make sure that it gets at least 60 ccs of liquid food source and/or fluids per day. To give you another way to translate that, a tablespoon contains 15 ccs therefore you will need to make sure that the 8-ounce puppy is given at least 4 tablespoons of food/fluid per day.

If the puppy is a *premature puppy*, you will need to feed him smaller amounts in more frequent feedings — every two hours for the first two to three days. Say, for instance the puppy is only about 3 oz at birth, you would feed him for the first time after he is warm, toasty, pink and active. It is always a good idea to keep Pedialyte on hand and use it for the first two tube feedings. Pedialyte contains important electrolytes, water and glucose, all very important for the puppy. It does not contain protein, however, so would only be useful for short-term use. You would feed him about 1.5 ccs of Pedialyte for a first feeding. Two hours later, you might increase it to 2 ccs of Pedialyte. For the next two hour feeding, you can mix the 2 cc feeding with half Pedialtye and half a formula like Esbilac. Three feedings after that, you could put him on Esbilac full strength. Keep feeding him an amount that is slightly under his body weight in ccs every two hours for the first day or so, weighing him often to make sure he is gaining weight.

If the puppy isn't gaining weight, increase the feedings until you are feeding him 1 cc per oz of body weight. Weigh him every morning to determine how much you will need to use for each feeding that day. If he weighs 4 oz, you would feed him 4 ccs per feeding every two hours for a day or so, then gradually spread out the feeding time to every 3 hours over the first week. You will need to re-measure the tube as the puppy grows in length. Check the mark you have made on the tube every morning by repeating the measuring procedure.

For a puppy who isn't premature, you only need to feed every 3–4 hours, and you can feed him his full weight translated from ounces into ccs, as discussed above. If your puppy weighs 7 oz, you would feed him about 4 ccs for the first two feedings, but after that you could increase the amount of liquids fed to 7 ccs, a cc or two at a time.

A word of caution here. For some reason, our society has gotten the idea that all sugar is bad. In fact, sugar, (which comes in many forms: glucose, dextrose, fructose, etc.) is necessary for life. The brain metabolizes ONLY sugar, so any feeding that doesn't contain glucose or another food source that the body will convert to sugar will be inadequate for long-term feeding purposes. Protein is necessary for cell growth. Pedialyte, because it doesn't contain protein, is not suitable for long-term feeding, therefore you will need to use a milk-based formula. For short term use, normal saline for sub-cutaneous hydration and Pedialyte for tube feeding is fine, but after a day of this, you will need instructions from your vet as to how to include protein feedings and glucose or your puppy will be starving in spite of the fact that he is well-hydrated.

Feed the full term puppy every three to four hours unless he is crying between meals. Then, either feed more often, or add a little bit more food to the feedings. Keeping the rough estimate of 1 cc per 1 oz of body weight in mind, and adding in that your puppy needs to be gaining weight every day, you will soon learn how much to feed, and how often to feed in order to keep your puppy content and growing. Weigh the puppy every day, at the same time of the day. Keeping a record is essential.

The sooner the puppy is able to go back with mom and nurse, the better. If a puppy is completely hand-reared, his growth rate will be much more erratic than the puppy that stays with his mom and nurses full time. Studies have shown that a completely hand-reared puppy at six weeks of age will be half the size of his siblings who were nursing from mom. You will find that the older hand-reared puppy can go on a bottle when he weighs 12 oz or so. By that time, he will eat much less often, often only about every 5 hours and sometimes less than that. Just offer the bottle and if he refuses, put it away and try again later. Your puppy will reach a point where he is simply too strong to tube feed. He will fight the tube feeding process so vigorously that you will have no choice but to move him on to other food sources including a bottle. You can try Nutra Stat — a paste nutritional substitute in a tube — on your finger (available at pet supply stores and mail order sources), or even try to get him to lap up baby food. Your vet can advise you on how to meet the puppy's nutritional needs.

Removing the feeding tube

Once you have syringed in the food source, crimp the tube near the baby's mouth and quickly withdraw it. Crimping will keep the tube from releasing the milk in the tube as it is withdrawn. Crimping has nothing to do with air or bubbles getting into the tummy. Crimping is about keeping the milk that remains in the tube, in the tube. If milk is coming out of the tube as it is withdrawn, there is a chance it can get into the trachea and be aspirated (inhaled into the lung) by the pup. Be sure to keep the tubes and syringes clean between feedings. You can wash the inside of the tube easily by simply withdrawing warm, slightly soapy water into the tube and syringe and then forcing it out. Rinse the same way. You must keep the tubes scrupulously clean and discard them if they show signs of wear. Discard the tube after one week of regular use and whatever you do, don't use the same feeding tube for years on end. They are pretty inexpensive and easy to find. The same applies to syringes — clean them thoroughly after each use, but discard after one week.

SUB-CUTANEOUS HYDRATION

The best-case scenario all the way around is for your vet to teach you how to do sub-cutaneous hydration. However, we are going back to the situation described before: You are sitting at three in the morning on a holiday weekend with a raging snowstorm outdoors and your puppy is showing all the signs of dehydration. What do you do? The answer is really quite simple. You read this book. You watch the DVD a couple of times and you hydrate the puppy.

If the puppy is severely dehydrated but not vomiting or having diarrhea, you will possibly need to tube feed him his weight in oz translated to ccs, as well as hydrate him under his skin with the same amount of warmed, IV fluids. Follow the instruction of your vet, but, generally speaking, 2–3 times per day will be sufficient for the sub-cutaneous hydration unless it is the only source of hydration available to you. Then, you will need to increase the times per day that you can hydrate using the sub-cutaneous technique. If a puppy gets dehydrated, a vet would administer 80–100 ml per kilogram of puppy weight sub-cutaneously or intravenously but he would deliver that amount of fluid with a full IV set-up versus a syringe. Depending on different diagnoses, a vet might choose to administer normal saline, dextrose and water or Lactated Ringers, but for keeping on hand in your emergency stores, Lactated Ringers is the best choice.

You will need to buy a bag of Lactated Ringers or another type of IV fluid. I include a bag in the Puppy Intensive Care Warming Box but you can also get them from your vet's office and from mail order and online catalogs. You will need a prescription to purchase mail order sources (see Resources).

Once you have begun to use your IV solution, keep it refrigerated. The container will be a clear plastic bag, sort of like a balloon. You can see through it and it will have lines on it to let you know how much is left in the bag. The top of the bag has a ring that allows you to hang the bag for IV fluids. Ignore the hanger. You are only interested in the small round rubber port. At the bottom of the bag will be a rubber port, usually yellow, but sometimes beige or white. It is that port that you will use to withdraw the amount of Lactated Ringers that you will need. Just push the needle into that port and withdraw what you need. Warm it gently and proceed to use it.

You will need a 20 cc syringe with a 22-gauge needle that is ¾ inch long. For smaller breeds, you can use a smaller syringe, and for larger breeds, you can certainly use a larger syringe, but the needle size will remain the same no matter how large the puppy is. These are available from almost any vet catalogs.

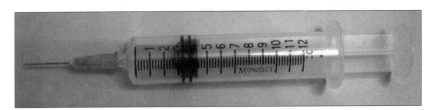

Using the thumb and first two fingers of your non-dominant hand, form a little "tent" at the back of the neck and shoulders of the puppy. I prefer to inject the fluid near the shoulder. If the puppy is wiggly, try to have a second person hold him for you. Hold the head of the puppy down and insert the needle under the skin right under your fingertip. Remember, you are only placing the needle under the skin, not into the muscle tissue underneath. Once the needle is under the skin, inject the IV fluid into that area. Inject it at a steady rate and don't worry about injecting it too quickly. Tube feeding needs to be done slowly and evenly, but sub-cutaneous hydration can just be placed under the skin at whatever rate your needle will allow you to inject it. The puppy's body will absorb it at the correct rate. Once it is injected, there will be a soft, watery little bubble there under the skin but it will absorb very quickly.

Once you have begun the process of hydrating your puppy, you need to check the color of his urine often. You will know the puppy is getting enough fluid when his urine is light straw colored. If it is still dark, he is still dehydrated. If the urine is almost colorless, you may be hydrating the puppy too much. By observing the color of

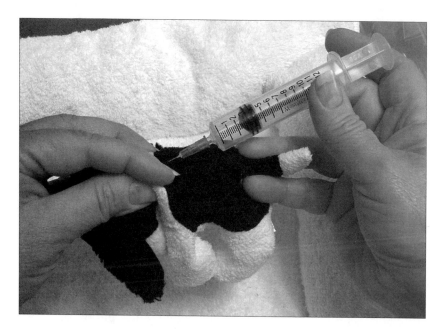

the urine, increase or decrease the amount of time between feedings or times when you use the sub-cutaneous technique. Also, check the specific gravity of the urine if you are in doubt about the puppy's hydration status using a DiaScreen test strip.

12

FINALLY...
THE END

WHEW! BET YOU THOUGHT WE'D NEVER MAKE IT

By this time, you are all eager to run to the stores, start making phone calls, and placing orders online for all of your supplies. You've already mentally found the perfect spot for your warming box. You're trying to figure out if you can justify spending the money for the portable power inverter. You have a plan for your own puppy intensive care unit. You have direction and goals, and you already have a growing confidence. In so many ways, my job is done.

As time goes on and you have had sick puppies of your own that you have saved, you are going to learn new techniques and skills and find even better products than I have discussed here. This is the best part about learning; it never stops. I hope that you will share those new and better ideas with me. I hope that you will tell me about new products and new sources as you find them so that I can share that information with others. I am available by email and am happy to answer questions that you may have. I always love to hear about your success stories using the techniques you've learned from this book. I hope that if you have questions or positive comments about the things I've written, you'll contact me. (Don't worry too much about sharing the negative comments with me. I'll be just as happy not to hear them.) My email address is: myrasavant@hotmail.com.

Those of us in the dog breeding community live in a culture within a culture. Only in our circles can we use the word "bitch" without feeling slightly naughty. With no other group of friends can you freely discuss the difficulties that your bitch had while "tied" with the stud. Who in the world knows what a "swimmer" is besides those of us who breed dogs? Where else can you chit-chat about chilled sperm versus frozen sperm? We are a unique group of people with different backgrounds, careers and aspirations, but we are, nevertheless, tightly bound by our love for dogs. We are all "dog people."

Sharing our knowledge and experience is called mentoring. My wish for all of you who are new to the dog breeding world is that you find a kind and generous mentor. My hope for those of you with knowledge and experience is that you will be those kind, generous mentors. If you find a vet who shares and teaches, treat him or her like gold. Truly, a caring, sharing vet is a treasure worthy of all of our appreciation.

Last of all, I wish you beautiful litters and twitchy, jerky, pink and plump puppies in every one.

AUTHOR BIOGRAPHY

As far back as I can remember, I have kept pets: mice, hamsters, rabbits, cats, dogs, birds, fish, chickens, goats, pigs, horses, a milk cow and snakes. I've bred most of these animals including tortoises, which are really hard to breed. I've had a life-long interest in the genetics of breeding and as a teenager, bred albino rabbits to whole color rabbits so that I could really fix in my mind the simple Mendelian theory of dominance and recessiveness in genetics. I fell in love with the first Cavalier I saw on a TV show and immediately wanted one. They are, as any Cavalier person will tell you, quite addictive and so I began showing them and eventually breeding them. My stud dog, Peakdowns Aidan, is ranked 4th in the US for stud dogs as he has produced many champions. Along the way, I also reared 10 children and I have 32 grandchildren, with two more on the way.

I started nursing school when I was 38. It was the science of nursing that attracted me; not the do-gooder sort of thing. I gravitated to labor/delivery and then neonatal intensive care because of my great interest in the reproductive system. I am still practicing nursing, although no longer in labor and delivery. I breed three to six litters of Cavaliers a year and am involved in showing. I have given seminars from Washington State to Florida and have many more scheduled. I truly enjoy this because it combines my interest in medicine, dogs and my interest in sharing this information with other breeders. I am currently finishing my next book on Reproduction and Whelping due in 2006. I live in Washington State with my husband Doug Harris and Cavaliers with lots of family nearby.

RESOURCES

Remember that prices change continually and any prices I note here are as of the time this book was written. Feel free to email me sources you have found for your equipment at myrasavant@hotmail.com. Information on ordering my Puppy Intensive Care Warming Box™ is below.

Chapter 2

Power converter/cigarette lighter adapter: Radio Shack, Costco and eBay or other auction sites. Cost: $25.00-$100.00.

Clear (almost clear) plastic box for warming box: 25"x 18"x7"; Sterilite® makes one this size that Walmart carries. Other brands work fine if approximately these dimensions. Removable tops are more common. Cost: $8.00

Heating Pad: I use a Sunbeam, model number 756-400, 12" by 15" with *no automatic shut off.* Cost: $16.00

Bumpered crate pad 24" X 18": pet supply stores, pet supply catalogs, on-line pet retailers. The best price I've found is the "Midwest Quiet Time Pet Bed" at Pet Edge, 1-800-738-3343, www.petedge.com

Chapter 3

Puppy pads (incontinence pads) 36" X 36": medical and pet supply companies or from myrasavant@hotmail.com. Cost: $12.00 each.

Chapter 4

Ear syringe: baby sections of drug stores, grocery stores and big department stores like Target. Cost: $4.00

Chapter 6

Fresh Frozen Plasma (FFP): Hemopet, 11330 Markon Drive, Garden Grove, California 92841, 1-714-891-2022, fax 714-891-2123. Call to place an order and to find out what quantity you will need on hand. For general information go to www.hemopet.com. Cost: 10-12 ccs $12.00 for small breeds.

Chapter 8

DiaScreen Reagent Test Strips: Kom Kare Company 1-800-273-1768, www.komkare.com. Cost: 100/$70.00. Once you open the package keep them in an airtight container and out of the light.

IV Solution (Lactated Ringers): KV Veterinary Supply, 3190 N. Road/ PO Box 245, David City, NE, 68632-0245, 1-800-423-8211, www.kvvet.com. Cost: $5.00 per liter bag. You will be required to have a prescription from your vet. I sell it as part of my "brand name here" but I do not sell them separately.

Heated Whelping Nest: Countryside Pet Supply, 2813 US Hwy 160 West Plains, MO 65775, 1-800-313-5737, www.countryside-vetsupply.com. Go to "dogs" then "heating pads and bowls" Cost: $250-300.00.

Oxygen canister: available from welding supply shops. Tanks are usually green or have some green on them. Cost: $60.00 small canister.

Oxygen regulator: buy the "threaded" variety as this is the only type that will work with the oxygen canister from a welding supply shop. Purchase through medical supply companies and auction sites such as eBay. It will usually describe it as being for "medical use". If in doubt, e-mail the person who is selling the regulator before you place a bid and ask them if it is for medical use. The prices really vary from $40 (a SUPER bargain)-$250.00.

Oxygen tubing: buy from the same places from which you bought the oxygen regulator.

Feeding tubes: buy tubes that are about 40 centimeters or 15 inches long. Do a computer search and find the clear silicone type easily. The red feeding tubes and syringes that fit them are available at Valley Vet Supply, 1-800-360-4838, www.valleyvet.com. Cost: $.75-$4.00

The Puppy Intensive Care Warming Box™ can be ordered directly from me at myrasavant@hotmail.com. I will give you current pricing. Payment can be made by check, money order or Pay Pal. Puppy Intensive Care Warming Boxes come in two types:

The Regular PIC Warming Box includes a plastic warming box with lid, a bumpered crate pad, heating pad without an automatic off feature, two feeding tubes with two syringes, one liter of IV fluid with two syringes with needles.

The Deluxe PIC Warming Box includes all of the above plus oxygen tubing and an oxygen regulator with a screw-on type connector.

PUPPY WEIGHT CHART

PUPPY	DATE	WEIGHT

PUPPY	DATE	WEIGHT

PUPPY	DATE	WEIGHT

PUPPY	DATE	WEIGHT

PUPPY	DATE	WEIGHT

PUPPY	DATE	WEIGHT

From Dogwise Publishing, www.dogwise.com, 1-800-776-2665

BEHAVIOR & TRAINING

Aggression In Dogs: Practical Mgmt, Prevention & Behaviour Modification. Brenda Aloff
Behavior Problems in Dogs, 3rd ed. William Campbell
Brenda Aloff's Fundamentals: Foundation Training for Every Dog DVD. Brenda Aloff
Bringing Light to Shadow. A Dog Trainer's Diary. Pam Dennison
Canine Body Language. A Photographic Gd to the Native Language of Dogs. Brenda Aloff
Clicked Retriever. Lana Mitchell
Dog Behavior Problems: The Counselor's Handbook. William Campbell
Dog Friendly Gardens, Garden Friendly Dogs. Cheryl Smith
Dog Language, An Encyclopedia of Canine Behavior. Roger Abrantes
Evolution of Canine Social Behavior, 2nd ed. Roger Abrantes
Mastering Variable Surface Tracking, Component Tracking (2 bk set). Ed Presnall
My Dog Pulls. What Do I Do? Turid Rugaas
New Knowledge of Dog Behavior (reprint). Clarence Pfaffenberger
On Talking Terms with Dogs: Calming Signals, 2nd edition. Turid Rugaas
On Talking Terms with Dogs: What Your Dog Tells You, DVD. Turid Rugaas
Positive Perspectives: Love Your Dog, Train Your Dog. Pat Miller
Right on Target. Taking Dog Training to a New Level. Mandy Book & Cheryl Smith
The Face In The Window: A Guide To Professional Dog Walking And Home Boarding. Dianne Eibner
Therapy Dogs: Training Your Dog To Reach Others. Kathy Diamond Davis
Training Dogs, A Manual (reprint). Conrad Most
Training the Disaster Search Dog. Shirley Hammond
Try Tracking: The Puppy Tracking Primer. Carolyn Krause
Winning Team. A Guidebook for Junior Showmanship. Gail Haynes
Working Dogs (reprint). Elliot Humphrey & Lucien Warner

HEALTH & ANATOMY, SHOWING

An Eye for a Dog. Illustrated Guide to Judging Purebred Dogs. Robert Cole
Annie On Dogs! Ann Rogers Clark
Canine Cineradiography DVD. Rachel Page Elliott
Canine Massage: A Complete Reference Manual. Jean-Pierre Hourdebaigt
Canine Terminology (reprint). Harold Spira
Dog In Action (reprint). Macdowell Lyon
Dogsteps DVD. Rachel Page Elliott
Performance Dog Nutrition: Optimize Performance With Nutrition. Jocelynn Jacobs
Puppy Intensive Care: A Breeder's Guide To Care Of Newborn Puppies. Myra Savant Harris
Raw Dog Food: Make It Easy for You and Your Dog. Carina MacDonald
Raw Meaty Bones. Tom Lonsdale
Shock to the System. The Facts About Animal Vaccination... Catherine O'Driscoll
The History and Management of the Mastiff. Elizabeth Baxter & Pat Hoffman
Work Wonders. Feed Your Dog Raw Meaty Bones. Tom Lonsdale

WARMING BOX ORDERING FORM

The regular warming box contains:
- Plastic box
- Heating pad
- Bumpered pad
- Bulb syringe
- Tube feeding supplies
- Sub-cutaneous hydration supplies

The deluxe warming box contains:
- The regular warming box
- Oxygen regulator
- Oxygen tubing

Select One: _____ Regular warming Box   _____ Deluxe warming Box

Name _____

Address _____

City, State, Zip _____

Phone Number _____

E-Mail Address _____

You may order the regular warming box for $175.00 and the deluxe warming box for $225.00 (prices include shipping and handling within the continental United States). PRICES ARE SUBJECT TO CHANGE. For current pricing or to order online please visit my website www.myrasavantharris.com.

Send payment to:
Myra Savant Harris
1561 Weathervane Ct
Fircrest, WA 98466

We accept check, money order or PayPal.